BEAU PEEP BOOK 13

From The

©1992
Express Newspapers plc
Researched by
Terry Greenwood

Published by

Annual Concepts Limited
One High Street
Princes Risborough
Buckinghamshire HP27 0AG
under licence from
Express Newspapers plc
ISBN 1 874507 023
Printed in Italy

£3.50

D0527704

BEAU PEEP

EGON

THE NOMAD

MAD PIERRE

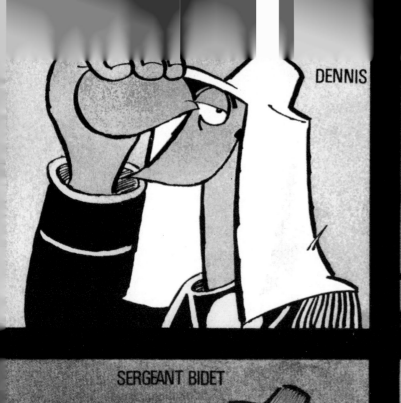

DENNIS

HAMISH

SERGEANT BIDET

COLONEL ESCARGOT

THE VULTURE

On the back cover of this book, you will see the unusual word "Triskaidekaphobia"- the fear of the number thirteen. Witness the frozen smiles in the photograph, on left, of artist, Andrew Christine, and writer, Roger Kettle, as they discuss the word "Bankmanageraphobia" the fear of book number thirteen not selling!

THE ADVENTURES OF LEGIONNAIRE
BEAU PEEP

FROM THE **Star** DAILY

TIME FOR THE OLD ANNUAL CHECK-UP!

KNOCK! KNOCK!

DOCTOR

3258

PAT!

THERE'LL BE NO PROBLEM FOR THIS WHIPPET-LIKE GREEK GOD OF A BODY!

TAKE A SEAT, FATSO.

I'M GOING TO ASK YOU SOME QUESTIONS ABOUT YOUR LIFESTYLE.

RIGHT!

3259

DO YOU EAT MUCH?

NOT ME – I'M A HEALTH FANATIC.

DRINK?

GOOD THINKING, DOC, I'LL HAVE A PINT!

I'LL GIVE HIM THE OLD REFLEX TEST WITH THE PENCIL.

CATCH!

COULD YOU GIVE ME A HAND TO GET IT OUT OF MY NOSE?

3261

EVERY SOLDIER IN THE LEGION SHOULD BE LEAN AND HARD...

3262

...NOT A SPARE OUNCE OF FLESH ON HIS FRAME— A FIGHTING MACHINE!

AND WHAT ARE YOU, PEEP?

A MINCING JALOPY, SIR.

REMEMBER, PEEP, I'M A DOCTOR.

I'M ALWAYS HERE READY TO LISTEN TO YOUR PROBLEMS.

3263

I'M SYMPATHETIC, SENSITIVE—

WHAT'S WRONG?

I'VE JUST NOTICED HOW UGLY YOU ARE.

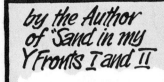

WHAT HAPPENS IN THE BEST SCIENCE FICTION?

SOME HARMLESS CREATURE TURNS INTO A RAVING MONSTER.

On top of Big Ben the sixteen foot sardine growled.

3273

I NEED NAMES FOR MY HERO AND HEROINE...

...SOMETHING IN KEEPING WITH THE SCIENCE-FICTION THEME.

Mr. Asteroid shook hands with Mrs. Milky Way.

3274

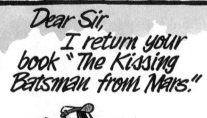

Dear Sir, I return your book "The Kissing Batsman from Mars."

It is, without doubt, the worst book I have ever read.

Love, Mum,

3275

3286

I SHOWED THAT PSYCHIATRIST!

HE TRIED TO TRICK ME WITH ONE OF THOSE WORD-ASSOCIATION TESTS.

WHAT DID YOU DO?

I SHOT HIM.

3303

THOSE PILLS FROM THE PSYCHIATRIST WILL HELP YOU, SIR.

YES, THEY'RE VERY GOOD. I LOVE THEM.

WITH THEIR PERT, ROUND LITTLE BODIES!

3304

HOW DID THE COLONEL GET ON AT THE PSYCHIATRIST?

HE WAS GIVEN SOME PILLS.

GOOD — IS HE TAKING THEM?

YES...

...TO LAS VEGAS. HE WANTS TO MARRY THEM.

3305

TO WIN COOKERY COMPETITIONS YOU HAVE TO USE SUBTLETY...

3321

...IT'S A CONTEST OF DELICATE TOUCH!

...ARE YOU SAYING MY "HADDOCK WITH LEEK IN GOB" WON'T WIN?

I'VE TAKEN YOUR ADVICE ABOUT SUBTLETY IN COOKING.

GOOD.

I'VE PREPARED "HADDOCK STUFFED WITH LEEKS."

SOUNDS PERFECT!

I MANAGED TO GET 28 IN!

3322

I HAVEN'T WON THE COOKERY CONTEST.

3323

THE RULES ALLOWED ONLY FISH AND LEEKS— THEY SAY I CHEATED.

HOW COME?

I RAN OUT OF LEEKS AND PAINTED A BLACK PUDDING GREEN.

3324

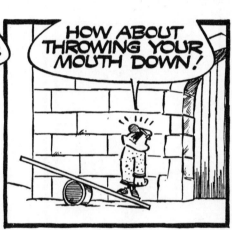

3325

3326

UP UNTIL NOW I'VE FAILED TO GET INTO THE FORT.

PERHAPS MY ATTEMPTS HAVE LACKED THE ELEMENT OF SURPRISE.

CRACKED IT!

3354

HA! THOSE FOOLS WILL THINK I'M AN INNOCENT MINSTREL!

BUT MY MOUTH ORGAN CONTAINS POISON DARTS!

MY DRUM CONCEALS MY SWORD!

AND MY SANDWICHES ARE IN THE GUITAR.

3355

THEY MUSTN'T GUESS THAT I'M ACTUALLY A BLOOD-CRAZED ASSASSIN.

I'LL DO A SONG TO STOP THEM BECOMING SUSPICIOUS.

OH, I'M DEFINITELY NOT A BLOOD-CRAZED ASSASSIN, BABY!

3356

Sand in my Y-Fronts IV

THIS IS HOPELESS! MY NOVELS NEVER SELL!

RIP!

MAYBE I SHOULD WRITE A POP SONG?

"*Sand in my Y-Fronts Boogie.*"

3390

THIS POP SONG I'M WRITING WILL SELL A MILLION!

WAH! WAH! SHOOBIE-DOOBIE! KISS ME! YEAH! YEAH! YEAH! DUM-DE-DUM!

ROMANTIC BALLADS ALWAYS DO WELL!

3391

LYRICS ARE VERY IMPORTANT IN POP SONGS.

PARTICULARLY IN THE SOFT, ROMANTIC BALLADS THAT I WRITE.

I WONDER WHAT RHYMES WITH "SLOBBERY"?

3392

3393

3394

3395

AW—LOOK, BEAU!

3402

A BIRD'S NEST WITH EGGS IN IT!

WHAT D'YOU THINK THEY'LL TURN OUT TO BE?

SCRAMBLED ON TOAST.

THE MOTHER MUST HAVE ABANDONED THEM.

RUBBISH!

3403

I KNOW ABOUT BIRDS AND SHE WOULDN'T DO THAT!

WHERE IS SHE THEN?

SHOPPING!

DENNIS, WHAT ARE YOU DOING?

3404

I'M GUARDING THESE EGGS FROM FOXES!

YOU KNOW A LOT OF FOXES WITH GRAPPLING IRONS, DO YOU?

PEEP IN THE
DAILY STAR
BRITAIN'S BRIGHTEST NEWSPAPER

DO YOU HAVE TURKEY FOR CHRISTMAS DINNER IN SCOTLAND?

OH, AYE—BUT NO' TOO MUCH.

OTHERWISE WE'D HAVE NO ROOM FOR THE MINCE AND TATTIES.

3459

SO YOU CELEBRATE CHRISTMAS MUCH THE SAME IN SCOTLAND?

AYE.

THE TREE, TURKEY, CRACKERS, DECORATIONS...

... JIMMY CLAUS.

3460

IT'S A LETTER FROM THE WIFE ABOUT HER PRESENT.

SHE'S NEVER HAPPY!

IF THE MARADONA BOOTS ARE TOO WEE SHE CAN CHANGE THEM.

3461

WHAT'S ALL THIS, DENNIS?

3533

I'M TRAINING TO BE A RADIO OPERATOR!

OH, I *SEE!* I THOUGHT YOU'D FINALLY GOT RIGGED UP WITH A PORTABLE BRAIN!

I'VE BEEN STUDYING ALL ABOUT RADIO OPERATING!

3534

LISTEN TO THIS... *DENNIS HERE!* UP AND UNDER!

THAT'S "OVER AND OUT," DENNIS.

GO ON — ASK ME ANYTHING ABOUT RADIO OPERATING!

535

OKAY — TELL ME ABOUT WAVELENGTHS.

WELL, I WEAR MINE SHORT SO THEY DON'T TANGLE IN THE EARPHONES.